Edited by

Ruth Armstrong
Melissa Black
Ewan Bleiman
Hannah J. E. Champion
Carrianne Sarah Colburn
Sarah Ferguson
Pasha Korniyenko
Rhea Lewis
James McCutcheon
Jennifer Wallace

in Edinburgh

Gwen Dickson
Emma Hodgkinson
Amy Lishman
Sophie Mayhew
Gavin Reed
Anna Steele
Kylie Wood

in Morpeth

Beth Armstrong
Catherine Bell
Katie Bradley
Elinor Brett
Ben Crothers
Meghan Diver
Alisa Logvinenko
Adrienne Madden
Stephanie McKeoun
Fiona Mulvenna

in Belfast

Stephanie Ashford
Peter Betty
Tom Davies
Zara Gibson
Matthew Langford
Emma Lewis
Victoria Nicholas
Kelly Louise Rees
Jessica Robins
Kara Marie Soccio
Rachael Thomas
Chris Wade

in Swansea

Francis Baker
Silvana D'Imperio
Uche Ebubedika
Vivian Gagariga
Pearl Mackie
Charlie-Mai Norris
Metta Phommavongsa
Anjuli Rogers
James Stevens
Rebecca Stokes

in London

Fifty Strong

Fifty poems chosen by teenagers for teenagers

Published by the South Bank Centre, London SE1 8XX

This selection © Royal Festival Hall 2004
Classification: Poetry
ISBN: 0-9544807-1-6

With thanks to Daisy Goodwin, Pat Hallam at the Northern Poetry Library,
Robyn Marsack at the Scottish Poetry Library, Sinéad Morrissey at the
Seamus Heaney Centre, David Woolley at the Dylan Thomas Centre and
Simon Smith, Miriam Valencia, Sue Mason and Charles Bainbridge at the
Poetry Library, SBC.

Contents

8

Introduction

In 2003 the Poetry Library at the South Bank Centre celebrated its fiftieth birthday, and to mark these celebrations we published an anthology – *Fifty Fifty* – with one poem from each of the Library's fifty years.

Then we decided to hand over editorial control to young people. We asked them to edit their own anthology – a collection of poems they wanted to recommend to other young people their own age. To do this we joined forces with four other wonderful poetry resources – the Scottish Poetry Library, the Northern Poetry Library, the Seamus Heaney Centre for Poetry and the Dylan Thomas Centre – and set up five groups of ten young people aged between 14 and 18 around the country.

Between them, working with poets Byron Beynon, Stephen Knight, Christian McEwen, Sinéad Morrissey and Paul Summers at these resources, this huge editorial panel read their way through countless books to track down the poems they wanted to see in their anthology. The result is *Fifty Strong*. Read on...

Sasha Hoare
Literature Education Officer
Royal Festival Hall, South Bank Centre

www.rfh.org.uk/education

Foreword
by Daisy Goodwin

Earlier this year Royal Festival Hall Education asked fifty teenagers to choose as many poems for an anthology to be circulated to every secondary school in the country. The idea of getting teenagers to choose poems is brilliant and long overdue; adolescence and poetry have a natural affinity.

Great poems have been written by teenagers – think of Keats, Rimbaud and the young Dylan Thomas and I think most people with a life-long love of poetry discovered its charms during the hormone-fuelled dramas of young adulthood. I remember at the age of fourteen first reading Yeats's 'He Wishes for the Cloths of Heaven' (one of the poems chosen) and being intoxicated by its sumptuous masochism. Here at last were words that perfectly expressed the torment of unrequited love (an occupational hazard of my teenage years). Finding the poem that translates the incoherent murmurings of one's heart into words is I think a key stage of adolescence, and I would argue a more useful one than some of the key stages our over-examined teenagers are expected to achieve.

The poems that are gathered together here make a truly refreshing collection – one that owes nothing to literary standard-bearing and everything to personal conviction. These poems are a primer for every young adult trying to make sense of an insensitive world. Some poems deal with the pain of love – the aforementioned Yeats and Carol Ann Duffy's 'Valentine', others look at tolerance, some deal with identity, a few even chronicle the disappointments of middle age.

The range of poets is eclectic: mostly modern they range from curriculum staples like Maya Angelou and Sylvia Plath, to relative newcomers like Henry Shukman. There are familiar poems and ones that I had never come across before. It is a tribute to the ability of

poetry to surf the generations that one of the poems included here
is Roger McGough's poem about being forty-seven years old and
undergoing the agony of missed opportunities. I suppose if there is
a common theme in this compassionate, salty, funny collection, it
is the importance of embracing life and making the most of every
opportunity it has to offer. In emergency room speak, the 'golden
hour' is the crucial time after an accident when medical intervention
can save lives. I think that adolescence is the 'golden hour' for
discovering poetry – I hope this exciting, thought-provoking collection
will change more than a few lives for the better.

Daisy Goodwin
6 July 2004

Daisy Goodwin is a poetry enthusiast who has edited five bestselling
poetry anthologies, has a poetry column in *You* magazine and presents
the BBC2 series *Essential Poems*.

The Seamus Heaney Centre for Poetry

The Seamus Heaney Centre for Poetry, affiliated to Queen's University, Belfast, opened in 2004. The Centre commemorates Seamus Heaney's Nobel Prize for Literature as well as the enormous contribution made to contemporary letters by Northern Irish writers more generally. Ciaran Carson is the inaugural director of the centre, and other writers working there include Medbh McGuckian, Glen Patterson, Sinéad Morrissey and Daragh Carville. The Seamus Heaney Centre provides teaching space and also houses a poetry library. Readings, lectures and symposiums are held at the Centre throughout the academic year.

www.qub.ac.uk/heaneycentre
tel: 02890 971 070
email: shc@qub.ac.uk

The Northern Poetry Library

2004 sees the 35th anniversary of the Northern Poetry Library, kept at Morpeth Library in Northumberland. First set up in 1969, it has grown into the largest collection of contemporary poetry in England outside London. It now comprises approximately 15,000 volumes, covering all the major poets who have emerged during the past three decades, as well as a wealth of small press and self-published work and extensive back runs of poetry and literary magazines. An unique feature of the Library is its postal loan service. Regardless of where a member lives, he or she can ring or email with their requests and the library will post the books to their home.

tel: Pat Hallam 01670 534 524
email: pahallam@northumberland.gov.uk

The Scottish Poetry Library

The Scottish Poetry Library is to be found off the Canongate, in Edinburgh's Old Town. Celebrating its twentieth birthday this year, the SPL has been established for the past five years in an award-winning new building. It houses about 30,000 items – books, literary magazines, CDs and audio-tapes – with a focus on contemporary Scottish poetry, but most countries and many languages are represented. It is open to all for borrowing (11.00 - 18.00 weekdays, 13.00 - 17.00 on Saturdays), which is free, and has an excellent children's section. It also runs an education programme and holds events.

www.spl.org.uk
tel: 0131 557 2876
email: inquiries@spl.org.uk

SCOTTISH POETRY LIBRARY
By leaves we live

The Dylan Thomas Centre

The Dylan Thomas Centre opened in 1995 as the principal venue for Arts Council England's UK Year of Literature. The Centre is an unique mix of arts centre, visitor attraction and public facility, including a café/bookshop and a restaurant for special functions. The Dylan Thomas exhibition, *Man and Myth*, attracts 50,000 visitors annually from all over the world, while the Centre runs a year-round programme of arts events, exhibitions and festivals, including the annual Dylan Festival and Wordplay Young People's Festival, which attracts some 7,000 young people every year.

www.dylanthomas.org
Tel: 01792 463 980

Dylan Thomas

The Poetry Library at the South Bank Centre

Anyone from anywhere can come into the Poetry Library and gain immediate access to the UK's biggest free-to-use collection of poetry. The Poetry Library was founded in 1953 and aims to stock all poetry published in the UK since about 1912, as well as a wide selection of international work. There is poetry for children and teachers, poetry on tape, CD and video, a huge collection of literary magazines, a unique press cuttings section and Library staff are always available to help you find the poem you want. The Library also provides writers and readers with up to date details of competitions, events, magazines, and courses. As poet John Hegley said of the Library, 'Use and enjoy this place. Burrow in. Borrow on'.

www.poetrylibrary.org.uk
Tel: 020 7921 0664
Email: info@poetrylibrary.org.uk

VOI

CES

Poems from the Scottish Poetry Library

chosen by
Ruth Armstrong Royal High School, Edinburgh
Melissa Black Royal High School, Edinburgh
Ewan Bleiman Royal High School, Edinburgh
Hannah J. E. Champion Knox Academy, Haddington
Carrianne Sarah Colburn Firrhill High School, Edinburgh
Sarah Ferguson Gracemount High School, Edinburgh
Pasha Korniyenko James Gillespie's High School, Edinburgh
Rhea Lewis James Gillespie's High School, Edinburgh
James McCutcheon Gracemount High School, Edinburgh
Jennifer Wallace Knox Academy, Haddington

Years S4 & S5

with **Christian McEwen**

Lucky Bag

Tattie scones, St Andra's banes,
a rod-and-crescent Pictish stane,
a field o whaups, organic neeps,
a poke o Brattisani's chips;
a clootie well, computer bits,
an elder o the wee free Kirk;

a golach fi Knoydart,
a shalwar-kemeez;
Dr Simpson's anaesthetics, *zzzzzzzz*,
a gloup, a clachan, a Broxburn bing,
a giro, a demo, Samye Ling;

a ro-ro in the gloaming,
a new-born Kirkcaldy
baby-gro; a Free State, a midden,
a chambered cairn –
yer Scottish lucky-bag, one for each wean;
please form an orderly   rabble.

Kathleen Jamie

Glossary
St Andra's banes St Andrew's bones
whaups curlews
neep`s turnips
poke bag
clootie well a well around which scraps of sick people's clothing are hung to indicate that the sickness is to be left behind at the well as a wish and gesture towards healing (old custom still followed in some parts of Scotland)
golach beetle or earwig
gloup a hole in a rock through which you can see the sea
clachan hamlet or village alehouse
bing slag-heap
midden dunghill (also a rubbish heap, as in 'your room's a midden!')
wean child

Valentine

Not a red rose or a satin heart.

I give you an onion.
It is a moon wrapped in brown paper.
It promises light
like the careful undressing of love.

Here.
It will blind you with tears
like a lover.
It will make your reflection
a wobbling photo of grief.

I am trying to be truthful.

Not a cute card or a kissogram.

I give you an onion.
Its fierce kiss will stay on your lips,
possessive and faithful
as we are,
for as long as we are.

Take it.
Its platinum loops shrink to a wedding-ring,
if you like.
Lethal.
Its scent will cling to your fingers,
cling to your knife.

Carol Ann Duffy

A chionn 's gu robh mi measail air

Thigeadh e thugam
nuair a bha e air mhisg
   a chionn 's gu robh mi measail air.

Dhèanainn tì dha
is dh'èisdinn ris
   a chionn 's gu robh mi measail air.

Sguir e den òl
is rinn mi gàirdeachas leis
   a chionn 's gu robh mi measail air.

Nist, cha tig e tuilleadh
is nì e tàir orm
   a chionn 's gu robh mi measail air.

Meg Bateman

Because I was so fond of him

He used to come to me
when he was drunk
  because I was so fond of him.

I'd make him tea
and listen to him
  because I was so fond of him.

He stopped the drink
and I was pleased for him
  because I was so fond of him.

Now he comes no more,
indeed he despises me,
  because I was so fond of him.

Meg Bateman (Translated by the poet)

The Visit

One night last summer
I was lying in bed, unable to sleep,
the balcony and front door
thrown open to the hot night,
when Death walked into the house.

He swept up to her bedside
without so much as a glance
in my direction, and set about
snapping something very fine
between his long, delicate fingers.

What are you doing? I hissed –
but soundlessly, as though on rails,
he slid backwards through the room again.
My little one frowned but only
in her own dream, and I lay

wondering what the threads were
that he'd broken so carefully.
And as I watched her breast rise and fall
my heart grew strangely heavy,
then heavy again with the knowledge.

Don Paterson

The Loch Ness Monster's Song

Sssnnnwhufffll?
Hnwhuffl hhnnwfl hnfl hfl?
Gdroblboblhobngbl gbl gl g g g g glbgl.
Drublhaflablhaflubhafgabhaflhafl fl fl –
gm grawwwww grf grawf awfgm graw gm.
Hovoplodok-doplodovok-plovodokot-doplodokosh?
Splgraw fok fok splgrafhatchgabrlgabrl fok splfok!
Zgra kra gka fok!
Grof grawff gahf?
Gombl mbl bl –
blm plm,
blm plm,
blm plm,
blp.

Edwin Morgan

Budgie Finds His Voice

from **The Life and Songs of the Budgie** *by Jake Strugnell*

God decided he was tired
Of his spinning toys.
They wobbled and grew still.

When the sun was lifted away
Like an orange lifted from a fruit-bowl

And darkness, blacker
Than an oil-slick,
Covered everything forever

And the last ear left on earth
Lay on the beach,
Deaf as a shell

And the land froze
And the seas froze

'Who's a pretty boy then?' Budgie cried.

Wendy Cope

Unto Us

Somewhere at sometime
They committed themselves to me
And so, I was!
Small, but I *was*.
Tiny in shape
Lusting to live
I hung in my pulsing cave.
Soon they knew of me
My mother – my father.
I had no say in my being
I lived on trust
And love
Tho' I couldn't think
Each part of me was saying
A silent Wait for me.
I will bring you love!
I was taken
Blind, naked, defenceless
By the hand of one
Whose good name
Was graven on a brass plate
in Wimpole Street,
and dropped on the sterile floor
of a foot operated plastic waste bucket.
There was no Queen's Counsel
To take my brief.
The cot I might have warmed
Stood in Harrod's shop window.
When my passing was told
My father smiled.
No grief filled my empty space.

My death was celebrated
With two tickets to see Danny La Rue
Who was pretending to be a woman
Like my mother was.

TelAviv, 8 February 1972
Spike Milligan

Kidspoem/Bairnsang

it wis January
and a gey dreich day
the first day Ah went to the school
so my Mum happed me up in ma
good navy-blue napp coat wi the rid tartan hood
birled a scarf aroon ma neck
pu'ed oan ma pixie an' my pawkies
it wis that bitter
said *noo ye'll no starve*
gie'd me a wee kiss and a kid-oan skelp oan the bum
and sent me aff across the playground
tae the place Ah'd learn to say
it was January
and a really dismal day
the first day I went to school
so my mother wrapped me up in my
best navy-blue top coat with the red tartan hood,
twirled a scarf around my neck,
pulled on my bobble-hat and mittens
it was so bitterly cold
said *now you won't freeze to death*
gave me a little kiss and a pretend slap on the bottom
and sent me off across the playground
to the place I'd learn to forget to say
it wis January
and a gey dreich day
the first day Ah went to the school
so my Mum happed me up in ma
good navy-blue napp coat wi the rid tartan hood,
birled a scarf aroon ma neck,
pu'ed oan ma pixie an' ma pawkies
it wis that bitter.

Oh saying it was one thing
but when it came to writing it
in black and white
the way it had to be said
was as if you were posh, grown-up, male, English and dead.

Liz Lochhead

A Note to the Difficult One

This morning I am ready if you are,
To hear you speaking in your new language.
I think I am beginning to have nearly
A way of writing down what it is I think
You say. You enunciate very clearly
Terrible words always just beyond me.

I stand in my vocabulary looking out
Through my window of fine water ready
To translate natural occurrences
Into something beyond any idea
Of pleasure. The wisps of April fly
With light messages to the lonely.

This morning I am ready if you are
To speak. The quick early rains
Of Spring are drenching the window-glass.
Here in my words looking out
I see your face speaking flying
In a cloud wanting to say something.

W S Graham

The Leader

I wanna be the leader
I wanna be the leader
Can I be the leader?
Can I? I can?
Promise? Promise?
Yippee, I'm the leader
I'm the leader

OK what shall we do?

Roger McGough

Notes

Lucky Bag by Kathleen Jamie

This wacky random collection of aspects of modern and multicultural Scotland, crossed with the abruptness and the traditional Scottish language, made us laugh! It provides some welcome relief from the postcard clichés of kilts and bagpipes.

Ruth Armstrong

Valentine by Carol Ann Duffy

We thought this poem was very unusual as it shows that love is not about fancy gifts but about emotions and meaning. A gift is nothing without thought behind it: a thought which can make the simplest gift become a passion. A lover's passion, a lover's possessiveness, a lover's love.

Pasha Korniyenko

Because I was so fond of him by Meg Bateman

We found this poem's message sharp and clear. The simple repetition was easy to relate to. We enjoyed the ironic ending, and the point it made: that too much listening can be harmful.

Rhea Lewis

The Visit by Don Paterson

In this poem, Don Paterson uses the issue of cot death to explore the emotions we all feel – the way we wish we could step in, stop the unstoppable.

Ewan Bleiman

The Loch Ness Monster's Song by Edwin Morgan

Edwin Morgan, the Scottish Poet Laureate, has portrayed one of Scotland's most famous characters. We chose this poem because we found it humorous, and it is also a challenge to try and read it out loud.

Jennifer Wallace

Budgie Finds His Voice by Wendy Cope

We found this poem highly comical. We liked the irony of the world ending and no one being left to hear the budgie finally speak.

Carrianne Sarah Colburn

Unto Us by Spike Milligan

This is a very thought-provoking poem which is really why we chose it. It starts off sweet and nice but finishes by guilt-tripping those who choose abortion. We didn't really agree with the last lines, and feel it is too strong and biased. But we thought it was very unusual and eerie to hear a poem in the voice of an aborted child.

James McCutcheon

Kidspoem/Bairnsang by Liz Lochhead

We found this poem light-hearted and funny. We identified with the two languages used within the poem and the formality of the language we learn in school.

Carrianne Sarah Colburn

A Note to the Difficult One by W S Graham

This poem sees Graham expressing his feelings over a dead friend, trying to say all that he could not say when the friend was alive. The poem has a fantastic clarity and freshness to it.

Ewan Bleiman

The Leader by Roger McGough

We chose this poem because it is so light-hearted. It is short, snappy and made everyone laugh. It really breaks up the collection of more serious poems. We all simply loved it.

James McCutcheon

THE
WEIGH
SORRO

Poems from the Northern Poetry Library

chosen by
Gwen Dickson
Emma Hodgkinson
Amy Lishman
Sophie Mayhew
Gavin Reed
Anna Steele
Kylie Wood

Years 9, 10, 11 & 12 from King Edward VI High School, Morpeth, Northumberland

with **Paul Summers**

As the Mist Leaves No Scar

As the mist leaves no scar
On the dark green hill,
So my body leaves no scar
On you, nor ever will.

When wind and hawk encounter,
What remains to keep?
So you and I encounter,
Then turn, then fall to sleep.

As many nights endure
Without a moon or star,
So will we endure
When one is gone and far.

Leonard Cohen

Drought

In the fiercest summer for years
gouts of sun sour milk in an hour,
rubbish simmers in streets which
steam with piss, swimming pools
pulse like tins of maggots
and all the time your postcards come.

Every village green turns brown,
reservoirs crack and rivers shrivel.
Each time I try to picture your face
sweat breaks over me
sudden as a storm
and all the time your postcards come.

Views of the Seine, the Tiber, the Nile,
necks of gondolas hooking through mist,
the Rhône, the Ganges, the Orinoco,
diving for danger at Acapulco.
All I ask's a screw, the shrink, a drink.
Honey, why do I always dream of death?

I can never slake this thirst,
can't eat, can't sleep, can't work, can't breathe,
my skin is scorched: the earth is tinder,
for nights I watch the hillside burn,
sparks hanging in the dark, like stars
and all the time your postcards come.

Heat silts up every artery,
the passages to my brain run dry.
Light thickens, clots, there is no shade.
Hair on my arms is bleached to straw.
You could put a match to me
but all the time, your postcards come.

Maura Dooley

Trust

Trust who?
Trust your friends
They can be back-stabbers
or spread lies about you
Trust the love of your life
Why? What if they cheat on you?
I can only trust one person
not everyone can manage that
Nothing can hurt more
than being betrayed
Trust only
yourself

Stacey Tully

Memory Unsettled

Your pain still hangs in air,
Sharp motes of it suspended;
The voice of your despair –
That also is not ended:

When near your death a friend
Asked you what he could do,
'Remember me,' you said.
We will remember you.

Once when you went to see
Another with a fever
In a like hospital bed,
With terrible hothouse cough
And terrible hothouse shiver
That soaked him and then dried him,
And you perceived that he
Had to be comforted,

You climbed in there beside him
And hugged him plain in view,
Though you were sick enough,
And had your own fears too.

Thom Gunn

Rendezvous

I have a rendezvous with Death
At some disputed barricade,
When Spring comes back with rustling shade
And apple-blossoms fill the air –
I have a rendezvous with Death
When Spring brings back blue days and fair.

It may be he shall take my hand
And lead me into his dark land
And close my eyes and quench my breath –
It may be I shall pass him still.
I have a rendezvous with Death
On some scarred slope of battered hill,
When Spring comes round again this year
And the first meadow-flowers appear.

God knows 'twere better to be deep
Pillowed in silk and scented down,
Where love throbs out in blissful sleep,
Pulse nigh to pulse, and breath to breath,
Where hushed awakenings are dear . . .
But I've a rendezvous with Death
At midnight in some flaming town,
When Spring trips north again this year,
And I to my pledged word am true,
I shall not fail that rendezvous.

Alan Seeger

He Wishes for the Cloths of Heaven

Had I the heavens' embroidered cloths,
Enwrought with golden and silver light,
The blue and the dim and the dark cloths
Of night and light and the half-light,
I would spread the cloths under your feet:
But I, being poor, have only my dreams;
I have spread my dreams under your feet;
Tread softly because you tread on my dreams.

W B Yeats

T𝚑   48

He stands, swaying,
Like a drunken man.
She sits, book in lap,
Staring at him with
Wild, defiant eyes.

They scream absurd
Obscenities at each other.
His drunken dance to the
Outsider is pathetic to see.
They are oblivious to all
Except their own anger.
Now and again there
Is a pause in the storm
As they gather strength
For part 2 of the battle.

And now she stands
Arms flailing out
Striking air. Suddenly,
No warning. He
Swings around his
Arm, and deals her
A heavy blow to the
Head. She is momentarily
Stunned, before falling
Backwards. Onto the
Couch. She'll forgive
Him again. Tomorrow.

Anne-Marie Thompson

Piano Solo

Years after my mother chose emptiness
at night I'd hear her at the piano
planting chords, waiting for them
to grow into something.

She never advanced from childhood
lessons. She'd crackle flat a dry page
of Bartok or *Anna Magdalena*
and make the house's spine go cold.

That was all her hesitant handfuls
conjured – misery, a lonely beginner
always beginning again, a weather
of notes I wished would pass.

They trickled onto my sheets
in the dark, each drop telling
how sad a woman could feel
even to have lost what made her sad:

Henry Shukman

War Torn

A Serbian shell tears
a gaping hole in the wall;
Mother writhes in pre-natal anguish.
Did I ask to be born into this?
A world of internal carnage;
from the natural agonies of birth
to this daily living death.
Through the rubble and debris
of dismembered human forms
I can see irreconcilable religions,
putrid hatreds in rancid fruition.
Karadzic's national rhetoric
is just a beguiling foil
for the shocking savagery
of soldiers' senseless actions;
families in fragments beyond repair.
A charred hand reaching out –
the fate of misplaced hopes.
The delicate tissue of peace –
a bloody, festering laceration.
She may resent the pain I'll bring,
but this will last fleetingly
when mine shall linger interminably.
I will be purged just like the rest,
unless the hands of the west
can part the waves of mixed blood.
In this muslim womb I can quickly absorb
the racial rancour towards my race;
time-held malice staining my enemies
like a rank, indelible sweat.
Inside I await that futile moment,
when mother, my birth is our regret.

Andrew Button

Tramp

This mad prophet
gibbers mid-traffic,
wringing his hands
whilst mouthing at heaven.

No messages for us.
His conversation is simply
a passage through time.
He points and calls.

Our uneven stares dissuade
approach. We fear him, his
matted hair, patched coat,
grey look from sleeping out.

We mutter amongst ourselves
and hope he keeps away. No
place for him in our heaven,
there it's clean, and empty.

Rupert M Loydell

Notes

As the Mist Leaves No Scar by Leonard Cohen

As a group, we chose this poem because it reflects both the potential futility of human relationships and the ethereal nature of love, moreover, the complex messages of the poem are related to the reader with a beautiful, poignant use of rhythm and language.

Gavin Reed

Drought by Maura Dooley

This poem was chosen because it portrays the pain and sufferings inflicted by love really well by comparing it to the pain and suffering caused by drought.

Sophie Mayhew

Trust by Stacey Tully

This poem was highly favoured amongst our group. Betrayal is a wound that grows deeper when breached by those closest to your heart.

Anna Steele

Memory Unsettled by Thom Gunn

This poem highlights the immense devotion, courage and love in a friendship. The deep emotion the poet evokes led the editorial team to a unanimous decision.

Amy Lishman

Rendezvous by Alan Seeger

We chose this poem because of the tragedy that the poet resigns himself to accept death as an integral part of war, and the fact that he is no longer frightened of it.

Gwen Dickson

He Wishes for the Cloths of Heaven by W B Yeats

This poem was chosen almost unanimously by the group, due to the succinct manner in which it conveys the absolute power of devotion, and the vulnerability reciprocal thereof; in addition, the poem's last line is universally applicable and this is reflected in its almost unrivalled popularity.

Gavin Reed

The Argument by Anne-Marie Thompson

A popular choice which portrays the horrific reality of domestic violence which commonly goes unnoticed but is evident in everyday society.

Anna Steele

Piano Solo by Henry Shukman

This poem was chosen because of its unusual combination of music and misery. The suffering of the mother is expressed through the piano but affects everything around her.

Emma Hodgkinson

War Torn by Andrew Button

We thought this poem conveys the grief of conflict and resignation to a certain fate. It is especially relevant to today's society, as wars are occurring due to cultural disparity.

Kylie Wood

Tramp by Rupert M Loydell

This poem conveys the common prejudices of today's world that people deny they have. Written from a non-judgemental point of view it creates a feeling of empathy from the reader.

Sophie Mayhew

DREAM AND ASPIRA

Poems from the Seamus Heaney Centre for Poetry

chosen by
Beth Armstrong
Catherine Bell
Katie Bradley
Elinor Brett
Ben Crothers
Meghan Diver
Alisa Logvinenko
Adrienne Madden
Stephanie McKeoun
Fiona Mulvenna

Years 12 & 13
From Methodist College Belfast

with **Sinéad Morrissey**

For the Child Who Became Christopher

May you come safe
     and flawless

May they gaze in awe
     at your small creased wrists
     and marvel
     at your perfect breath
     and ordinariness

May they gurgle at you
     and drool gratitude

May your gaze and grip
     reassure them

May your limbs
     be proper and deft
     your crawl furious
     your falls neat

May your most frightening dark
     be in stories
     the deepest thunder
     over the hills yonder

May no-one fence you round
     with their own hopes
     or shawl you in their dreams

May your teachers learn
     from your crazes

and amazements

May your friends
be a bridge to cross over
in any weather

May you have without too much wanting
and want without too much need

May there be sacred places
to return to

May stones fall short
and only low branches break
and swings miss you
on the way back.

Roger Hull

The Boy with a Cloud in his Hand

He hasn't got much: not a roof,
nor a job, nor any great hopes,
but he's got a cloud in his hand
and he thinks he might squeeze
till the rain falls over the town,
and he thinks he might tease
the cottonwool fluff into strands
of thin mist, and blank everything out,
and he thinks he might blow
this dandelion clock so high,
it will never come down, and he thinks
he might eat it, a taste of marshmallow
sliding inside him, filling him up
with emptiness, till he's all space,
and he thinks, when he's hollow and full,
he might float away.

Sheenagh Pugh

Polly's Tree

A dream tree, Polly's tree:
  a thicket of sticks,
    each speckled twig

ending in a thin-paned
  leaf unlike any
    other on it

or in a ghost flower
  flat as paper and
    of a color

vaporish as frost-breath,
  more finical than
    any silk fan

the Chinese ladies use
  to stir robin's egg
    air. The silver-

haired seed of the milkweed
  comes to roost there, frail
    as the halo

rayed round a candle flame,
  a will-o'-the-wisp
    nimbus, or puff

of cloud-stuff, tipping her
  queer candelabrum.
    Palely lit by

snuff-ruffed dandelions
  white daisy wheels and
    a tiger-faced

pansy, it glows. O it's
  no family tree,
    Polly's tree, nor

a tree of heaven, though
  it marry quartz-flake,
    feather and rose.

It sprang from her pillow
  whole as a cobweb,
    ribbed like a hand,

a dream tree. Polly's tree
  wears a valentine
    arc of tear-pearled

bleeding hearts on its sleeve
  and, crowning it, one
    blue larkspur star.

Sylvia Plath

Chapter 10:
The Meeting Dream

(from *The Adoption Papers*)

If I picture it like this is hurts less
We are both shy
though our eyes are not,
they pierce below skin.
We are not as we imagined:
I am smaller, fatter, darker
I am taller, thinner
and I'd always imagined her hair dark brown
not grey. I can see my chin in hers
that is all, though no doubt
my mum will say, when she looks at the photo,
she's your double she really is.

There is no sentiment in this living-room,
a plain wood table and a few books.
We don't cuddle or even shake hands
though we smile sudden as a fire blazing
then die down.
Her hands play with the wedding-ring,
I've started smoking again.

We don't ask big questions even later by the shore.
We walk slow, tentative as crabs
No, so what have you been doing the past 26 years.
Just **what are you working at**, stuff like that.

Ages later I pick up a speckled stone
and hurl it into the sea,
is this how you imagined it to be?
I never imagined it.
Oh. I hear the muffled splash.
It would have driven me mad imagining,
26 years is a long time.

Inside once more I sip hot tea
notice one wood-framed photo.
The air is as old as the sea.
I stare at her chin till she makes me look down.
Her hands are awkward as rocks.
My eyes are stones washed over and over.

If I picture it like this it hurts less

One dream cuts another open like a gutted fish
nothing is what it was;
she is too many imaginings to be flesh and blood.
There is nothing left to say.
Neither of us mentions meeting again.

Jackie Kay

Alternate

Well, she was tired, I suppose;
she'd been up watching videos till late

and she wasn't really interested,
but I nuzzled, made a pest

of myself, and she played along,
sleepily. No spark, but I needed

the closeness. I'll take what's on offer,
these days. Then she goes all soft

suddenly, relaxes, kisses back,
and I miss a breath. But she's looking

past me somehow, and I know
the look: I know what she's doing.

She's making a *what if*, rewriting
the script. This man, not that...

and she moves like water, and it's perfect,
except it's all for him. I hold her,

not speaking, because it's not my voice
that belongs with this. I'd only

spoil it for her. I let him come
in my body, pulsing, foaming,

eyes full of stars. Then I turn and lie
facing away, because I'm crying.

Sheenagh Pugh

I wake up in your bed.
I know I have been dreaming

I wake up in your bed. I know I have been dreaming.
Much earlier, the alarm broke us from each other,
you've been at your desk for hours. I know what I dreamed:
our friend the poet comes into my room
where I've been writing for days,
drafts, carbons, poems are scattered everywhere,
and I want to show her one poem
which is the poem of my life. But I hesitate,
and wake. You've kissed my hair
to wake me. *I dreamed you were a poem*,
I say, *a poem I wanted to show someone* . . .
and I laugh and fall dreaming again
of the desire to show you to everyone I love,
to move openly together
in the pull of gravity, which is not simple,
which carries the feathered grass a long way down the upbreathing air.

Adrienne Rich

Wishbone

My wish is simple, Lord, though open to
derision. I should like to see my hips
swell out a bit, and of their own volition mix
up courtly motions in my skirt, as You
presumably ordained; and feel it right
to wear those tiny nether garments in Your sight.

Concomitant on that, I'd like to smell
of roses of Arabia, and fold
the archaeology of love in cold
and fleshly audit, rather as the fell
administers its weathers. Let me cease
spotting the blemish in the human face.

The thought that men are incidental to
the solemn mysteries – *viz*. birth – goes hard,
though envy's not my motive. The petard
I want to choke on's more to do
with provenance, the inside rationale,
placenta to that Gioconda smile.

Well, if not literal flesh and blood, I hope
to bring back traces of a gentler birth
though it may be that vatic Mother Earth
is hard as nails, and various as rope.
But sure I'll be less as a sounding brass –
and more forthcoming than Tiresias!

Humbug detectors, bottomless yearnings, I
look forward most to meeting in my breast
some nameless arctic leopard, atavist
and poet, built to cleanse the eye
of dreams, kick up the snow a little, lease
each sinew to the ice-cap, and lie down in peace.

William Scammell

Here I Am

Here I am
forty-seven years of age
and never having gone to work in ladies' underwear

Never run naked at night in the rain
Made love to a girl I'd just met on a plane

At that awkward age now between birth and death
I think of all the outrages unperpetrated
opportunities missed

The dragons unchased
The maidens unkissed
The wines still untasted
The oceans uncrossed
The fantasies wasted
The mad urges lost

Here I am
getting on for seventy
and never having stepped outside for a fight

Crossed on red, pissed on rosé (or white)
Pretty dull for a poet, I suppose, eh? Quite.

Roger McGough

The Philosopher

Three blank walls, a barred window with no view,
A ceiling within reach of the raised hands,
A floor blank as the walls.

And, ruling out distractions of the body –
Growth of the hair and nails, a prison diet,
Thoughts of escape –

Ruling out memory and fantasy,
The distant tramping of a gaoler's boots,
Visiting mice and such,

What solace here for a laborious mind!
What a redoubtable and single task
One might attempt here:

Threading a logic between wall and wall,
Ceiling and floor, more accurate by far
Than the cob-spider's.

Truth captured without increment of flies:
Spinning and knotting till the cell became
A spacious other head

In which the emancipated reason might
Learn in due time to walk at greater length
And more unanswerably.

Robert Graves

Caged Bird

A free bird leaps
on the back of the wind
and floats downstream
till the current ends
and dips his wing
in the orange sun rays
and dares to claim the sky.

But a bird that stalks
down his narrow cage
can seldom see through
his bars of rage
his wings are clipped and
his feet are tied
so he opens his throat to sing.

The caged bird sings
with a fearful trill
of things unknown
but longed for still
and his tune is heard
on the distant hill
for the caged bird
sings of freedom.

The free bird thinks of another breeze
and the trade winds soft through the sighing trees
and the fat worms waiting on a dawn-bright lawn
and he names the sky his own.

But a caged bird stands on the grave of dreams
his shadow shouts on a nightmare scream
his wings are clipped and his feet are tied
so he opens his throat to sing.

The caged bird sings
with a fearful trill
of things unknown
but longed for still
and his tune is heard
on the distant hill
for the caged bird
sings of freedom.

Maya Angelou

...es

...or the Child Who Became Christopher by Roger Hull

This poem captures the dream of the poet for the new life that will become 'Christopher'. I was particularly drawn to it because the poet wants the child's life to be full of experiences – both good and bad. The discreet form of the poem also greatly added to my enjoyment of it, as you do not pick up on it until having read the final stanza.

Beth Armstrong

The Boy with a Cloud in his Hand by Sheenagh Pugh

I love the idea that the boy with a cloud in his hand may not own material possessions or have a job, but that he can still dream of his hopes and ambitions, which this poem places more emphasis on than any material object.

Stephanie McKeown

Polly's Tree by Sylvia Plath

I am a great fan of Plath's work, and 'Polly's Tree' fits perfectly into the theme. It contains so many beautiful images from the 'robin's egg air' to the 'white daisy wheels' and I believe its effectiveness lies in its sheer simplicity. It really is as precious as the 'blue larkspur star'.

Ben Crothers

Chapter 10: The Meeting Dream (from *The Adoption Papers*) by Jackie Kay

I chose this poem as it was such an open emotional appraisal of a dreamed hope and the feeling of being left unfulfilled. It is a common theme – disappointment over an event you've played in your head so many times it's means as much as any real event. In a modern world we try not to expect too much but human emotion drives us towards the desire for what we really want.

Adrienne Madden

Alternate by Sheenagh Pugh

This poem appealed to me because it was an unusual slant on the theme of dreams and aspirations. Instead of focusing on one's own ambitions, it highlights how a person's dreams can affect and hurt others. The effect is very moving, and it struck me as a very original poem.

Fiona Mulvenna

'I wake up in your bed, I know I have been dreaming' by Adrienne Rich

I like this poem because it contains two dreams, the dream to become a brilliant poet and the dream of wanting to show off someone you love. The poem appealed to me because of the imagery of love throughout.

Catherine Bell

Wishbone by William Scammell

This poem is ironic in that the poet's dream is not simple in the least, as the opening line would lead us to believe. The poem is a complex but interesting view on life as a woman and the trials life sets like birth. The ending of the poem mirrors the beginning as 'lie down in peace' is ironically placed in this fast and continuously surprising poem.

Meghan Diver

Here I Am by Roger McGough

I love this poem for its sentiments. Even at the age of 17 looking back we could have had so much more fun had we all done something a little more extreme and unconventional, and with hindsight being good looks like more trouble than it's worth. The poem also shows us why we never do this.
The poet's life slips from 47 to 70 as he thinks about his dreams, and even now I feel too lazy to face the consequences of any trouble I feel like making!

Elinor Brett

Caged Bird by Maya Angelou

This poem automatically captured my attention through its pure, raw strength. The parallels made between the caged bird and man struck me as being a common aspiration of freedom throughout nature.

Katie Bradley

MEDD

T MA

YOU T

WYL:

KES

HINK

Poems from the Dylan Thomas Centre

chosen by
Stephanie Ashford
Peter Betty
Tom Davies
Zara Gibson
Matthew Langford
Emma Lewis
Victoria Nicholas
Kelly Louise Rees
Jessica Robins
Kara Marie Soccio
Rachael Thomas
Chris Wade

Year 10 from Cefn Hengoed Community School, Swansea

with **Byron Beynon**

In the desert

In the desert
I saw a creature, naked, bestial,
Who, squatting upon the ground,
Held his heart in his hands,
And ate of it.
I said, 'Is it good, friend?'
'It is bitter – bitter,' he answered;
'But I like it
Because it is bitter,
And because it is my heart.'

Stephen Crane

In my craft or sullen art

In my craft or sullen art
Exercised in the still night
When only the moon rages
And the lovers lie abed
With all their griefs in their arms,
I labour by singing light
Not for ambition or bread
Or the strut and trade of charms
On the ivory stages
But for the common wages
Of their most secret heart.

Not for the proud man apart
From the raging moon I write
On these spindrift pages
Nor for the towering dead
With their nightingales and psalms
But for the lovers, their arms
Round the griefs of the ages,
Who pay no praise or wages
Nor heed my craft or art.

Dylan Thomas

Esgidiau

(mewn amgueddfa, lle cedwid pethau'r
***Résistance* a'r Natsïaid)**

Blinder traed yn ein gyrru
a hi'n bnawn Sul yn Oslo
i araf-fyd amgueddfa
a chanfod
esgidiau plant;
catrodau a chatrodau ohonynt,
yn rhesi a rhesi destlus;
a chyn nwyo'r rhai bach un pnawn,
rhoddwyd trefn arnynt.

Mor ddiystyr yw esgidiau, heb draed.

Clymwyd careiau
esgidiau cryfion di-draul
heb i byllau dŵr dasgu ar eu traws
na sgathru waliau wrth ddringo,
heb dympandod y lledr
na rhychiadau o ôl cwympo,
y baglu anorfod, na'r bracso;
rhai'n argoeli
braidd-dysgu-cerdded.

A fel 'na y tyfodd un bothell
ar bnawn Sul,
wrth wylio hil
a'i thranc,
mor ddi-stŵr
yn nhraed eu sanau.

Menna Elfyn

Shoes

(in a museum of Résistance and Nazi memorabilia)

Way-worn by Oslo
one Sunday afternoon
our feet sought out
a museum's gentler pace:

a museum of shoes,
regiments and regiments
in row on neat row
of children's shoes,
removed and set down in an orderly manner
before the little ones were gassed of an afternoon.

So bereft of meaning are shoes without feet.

Stout little shoes,
shoes with laces tied and hardly worn –
unsplashed through puddles,
unscuffed against bark,
not a toecap grazed to bewail a fall,
no leather creased into durable smiles
by the deft percussion of tiny soles;
shoes hinting of
just-beginning-to-walk.

And that's how
there erupted this blister –
through bearing witness
one Sunday afternoon
to a people and the manner
they met their end
so noiselessly
in their stockinged feet.

Menna Elfyn (Translated by **Nigel Jenkins**)

Leisure

What is this life if, full of care,
We have no time to stand and stare.

No time to stand beneath the boughs
And stare as long as sheep or cows.

No time to see, when woods we pass,
Where squirrels hide their nuts in grass.

No time to see, in broad daylight,
Streams full of stars like skies at night.

No time to turn at Beauty's glance,
And watch her feet, how they can dance.

No time to wait till her mouth can
Enrich that smile her eyes began.

A poor life this if, full of care,
We have no time to stand and stare.

W H Davies

Swonzee Boy See?

Sorrite livin up yur
bifarout like few wonoo gerrinter town.
Yea I knowzitser city burrile olliz call it town.

I wuz born downer Sanfeels see,
noffar from weara Soshul is now
– airza joke forew.

Ayve done some fancy work rounair, avenay?
Sorl been tarted up like
roun byer Lehjer un South Dock.
Ew doan see flats ly cat up Blineymice.
Meenmy brother ewster dive inner dock
– few trydit now ewed crackew ed onner yot.

I been inat Marrytime Muzeeum.
Ayve got bitvanole Mumbles train air.
I memberat wen I wozzer kid.
Ewster put ape nees onner line
forrer trainster go overum sozaid gedas bigas pennys
– tryum inner chewing gum machines see?

Awler family ewseter go downer Bracelet inner summer
on at ole train
evenee ole man.
Ew could mover seats
sowzew couldawl sitagether.

Ay still maker lotter fuss bout at train
ewed think it wuzy oney thingutad been taken fromair.

David Hughes

Alys at the Zoo

It was a wonderland for you:
The leopards leapt and parrots flew

Out of your picture-book's square cage
On to the living eye's quick page.

You raised your little arms to be
Lifted into the company

Of seal and penguin in their pool,
Wanting to join and go to school

With chimpanzee and kangaroo
And elephant and cockatoo,

To pat the tigers in their pen,
To play with and to comfort them.

We too seemed to hear them call
For comfort over bars and wall,

Their life-force trapped, their splendour tamed,
And went home quiet, a bit ashamed.

Raymond Garlick

Harry Pushed Her

Harry pushed her;
He pushed her around;
He pushed his sister.
Before school, after school;
On weekends.
He pushed his sister;
He had no friends.
He pushed her – school-holidays
And Christmas time.
The children always
Sang their made-up rhyme:
"Harry push her, push her now!
Harry push the crazy cow!"
Harry pushed her without strain:
Through snow, sunshine, wind and rain.
She smiled strangely
And never said a word.
He pushed her for years –
It was so absurd.
Harry was twelve;
His sister twenty-three.
Harry never had a childhood like me.
Harry pushed her without a care;
He pushed his sister in her wheelchair.

Peter Thabit Jones

Waun Fair

They sold apples and geese and ponies
In the fair upon the moor
On fine September mornings
Years and years ago.

They cursed and laughed and haggled
Until the deals were done,
And lifted pots of beer
Against the autumn sun.

And wily folk worked wonders
Upon the moor of old,
But the florins lasted longer
Than they who bought and sold.

And now the moor is silent,
With rougher winds to freeze
The lips of a Rhymney poet
Making bargains with the breeze.

Idris Davies

Dveře

Jdi a otevři dveře.
   Třeba je tam venku
   strom, nebo les,
   nebo zahrada,
   nebo magické mêsto.

Jdi a otevři dveře.
   Třeba tam pes škrábe.
   Treba je tam tvář,
   nebo oko,
   nebo obraz
           obrazu.

Jdi a otevři dveře.
   Kdyz je tam mlha,
   spadne.

Jdi a otevři dveře.
   I kdyby tam byla jen
   tíkající tma,
   kdyby tam bylo jen
   duté vanutí,
   i kdyby tam
         nic
          nebylo,
jdi a otevři dveře.

Aspon
průvan
bude.

Miroslav Holub

The door

Go and open the door.
　Maybe outside there's
　a tree, or a wood,
　a garden,
　or a magic city.

Go and open the door.
　Maybe a dog's rummaging.
　Maybe you'll see a face,
or an eye,
or the picture
　　　　　of a picture.

Go and open the door.
　If there's a fog
　it will clear.

Go and open the door.
　Even if there's only
　the darkness ticking,
　even if there's only
　the hollow wind,
　even if
　　　nothing
　　　　　is there,
go and open the door.

At least
there'll be
a draught.

Miroslav Holub
(Translated by **Ian Milner**)

There are nights that are so still

from *The Other*

There are nights that are so still
that I can hear the small owl calling
far off, and a fox barking
miles away. It is then that I lie
in the lean hours awake, listening
to the swell born somewhere in the Atlantic
rising and falling, rising and falling
wave on wave on the long shore
by the village, that is without light
and companionless. And the thought comes
of that other being who is awake, too,
letting our prayers break on him
not like this for a few hours,
but for days, years, for eternity.

R S Thomas

Notes

In the desert by Stephen Crane

This poem shows us what a man does to himself when he finds out that he has been nasty to other people. It also reminded me of the war in Iraq and more generally the horror of war.

Matthew Langford

In my craft or sullen art by Dylan Thomas

This poem really makes people think hard. Dylan Thomas creates an evening atmosphere. I would recommend it to other young people who want to concentrate, keep looking at the poem and try to work it out.

Tom Davies

Shoes by Menna Elfyn

This poem is based on a very disturbing period in history and it makes you think of all the children who died in the Holocaust. However it is clever that Menna Elfyn takes the shoes and transforms them into such a moving and thought-provoking poem. The fact that the children's shoes were taken off them before they were killed is so sad. It is interesting that the poem focuses on shoes instead of the sadness of the children being gassed.

Zara Gibson, Emma Lewis and Rachael Thomas

Leisure by W H Davies

I chose this poem because I thought it was calming. I liked the rhyme, and it tells me time passes quickly and that we should not waste it.

Jessica Robins

Swonzee Boy See? by David Hughes

I like the language and I would recommend the poem for the enjoyment, fun and challenge it presents to the reader.

Victoria Nicholas

Alys at the Zoo by Raymond Garlick

I enjoyed reading it because it has a good twist at the end and puts across an important point. It made me think about how animals are treated, that they are trapped behind bars for our enjoyment.

Peter Betty and Chris Wade

Harry Pushed Her by Peter Thabit Jones

It has an unusual twist at the end. You should not judge people until you know the whole story. When I first read it I immediately thought Harry was bullying his sister, but we discover something different by the end of the poem.

Stephanie Ashford, Peter Betty and Rachael Thomas

Waun Fair by Idris Davies

This poem tells us about a moorland fair years ago. I like it because it flows well and rhymes.

Kelly Louise Rees

The door by Miroslav Holub

I enjoyed reading this poem because it describes people's feelings about the un-known. I think the door represents a person's fear that is holding him or her back.

Zara Gibson

There are nights that are so still by R S Thomas

The poet talks about the night and it sounds beautiful. The mood of the poem is intense and realistic.

Kelly Louise Rees

THE

THE

END

N?

Poems from the Poetry Library at the South Bank Centre

chosen by
Francis Baker
Silvana D'Imperio
Uche Ebubedika
Vivian Gagariga
Pearl Mackie
Charlie-Mai Norris
Metta Phommavongsa
Anjuli Rogers
James Stevens
Rebecca Stokes

Years 12 & 13 from St Francis Xavier Sixth Form College, London

with **Stephen Knight**

Crimewatch

In some quite ordinary bathrooms and kitchens
have been committed the most marvellous murders
such as, witnessed by sadists,
would have made their upright members like girders!

In sinks and coppers and wash-basins and bath-tubs
the victimised corpses have been dismembered
and there are thousands of real life crime books
that take good care that this is remembered.

Radio commentators, like black-fairy-story-tellers,
have gloated over the execution of Crippen and others
without for a moment thinking
that in a way he and they are brothers . . .

I believe the deep psychological fact is
that what they admire is the man with the nerve
to put some great cruelty into practice –
like Genghis Khan or Hitler, who would never swerve

or show weakness over Jews, gypsies,
liberals, psychopaths or reds.
After every battle Genghis had to have his
fixed quota of a thousand heads.

All of these determined lunatics
fascinate the meek and the mild
who could never quite screw up their courage
to murder a child,

and perhaps even less to saw up a body
or hack one to pieces;
so these murderers act as a sort of safety-valve.
That is my thesis.

Gavin Ewart

Empires

All the dead Imperia . . . They have gone
Taking their atlases and grand pianos.
They could not leave geography alone.
They conquered with the thistle and the rose.
To our forefathers it was right to raise
Their pretty flag at every foreign dawn
Then lower it at sunset in a haze
Of bugle-brass. They interfered with place,
Time, people, lives, and so to bed. They died
When it died. It had died before. It died
Before they did. They did not know it. Race,
Power, Trade, Fleet, a hundred regiments,
Postponed that final reckoning with pride,
Which was expensive. Counting up the cost
We plunder morals from the power they lost.
They ruined us. They conquered continents.
We filled their uniforms. We cruised the seas,
We worked their mines and made their histories.
You work, we rule, they said. We worked; they ruled.
They fooled the tenements. All men were fooled.
It still persists. It will be so, always.
Listen. An out-of-work apprentice plays
God Save the Queen on an Edwardian flute.
He is, but does not know it, destitute.

Douglas Dunn

The Dead

Revolving in oval loops of solar speed,
Couched in cauls of clay as in holy robes,
Dead men render love and war no heed,
Lulled in the ample womb of the full-tilt globe.

No spiritual Caesars are these dead;
They want no proud paternal kingdom come;
And when at last they blunder into bed
World-wrecked, they seek only oblivion.

Rolled round with goodly loam and cradled deep,
These bone shanks will not wake immaculate
To trumpet-toppling dawn of doomstruck day:
They loll forever in colossal sleep;
Nor can God's stern, shocked angels cry them up
From their fond, final, infamous decay.

Sylvia Plath

Ceneri

Ceneri
di cose morte, di mali perduti,
di contatti ineffabili, di muti
sospiri;

vivide
fiamme da voi m'investono nell'atto
che d'ansia in ansia approssimo alle soglie
del sonno;

e al sonno,
con quei legami appassionati e teneri
ch'ànno il bimbo e la madre, ed a voi ceneri
mi fondo.

L'angoscia
insidia del varco, io la disarmo. Come
un beato la via del paradise,
salgo una scala, sosto ad una porta
a cui suonavo in altri tempi. Il tempo
ha ceduto di colpo.
    Mi sento,
con i panni e con l'anima di allora,
in una luce di folgore; al cuore
una gioia si abbatte vorticosa
come la fine.
    Ma non grido.
    Muto
parto dell'ombre per l'immenso impero.

Umberto Saba

Ashes

Ashes
of dead things, ills forgotten,
contacts unspeakable, dumb
regrets;

red-glowing
the flames from you envelop me, even as
borne on from care to care, I near the sill
of sleep.

And so to sleep,
in bonds like those impassioned and yet tender
that bind the child and mother, and to you, embers,
I yield.

The anguish
in ambush at the pass I conquer. Like
a blessed soul mounting to Paradise
I climb a stair and pause beside a gate
where once I knocked in other times. The years
have crumbled away.
                    And I feel,
with soul and garments as in bygone days,
a splendor as of lightning; on my heart
in whirling transport exultation breaks . . .
The end then?
                    But I make no outcry.
                                        Mute
I leave the shadows for the vast empire.

Umberto Saba (Translated by **Thomas G. Bergin**)

Your Sorrow

You take your sorrow with you when you leave.
However wide the sea or sky between,
the journey's end will bring you no reprieve.
Peter Sacks

But what if you change
and your sorrow becomes
your memory, a broken bone,
a finger that heals strangely
forever crooked for the world to see
so even your thoughts don't match up –
and yet there's no pain left.

Isn't there a place
that would make you forget?
A sky that would make you
disagree with yourself – ?
A sea that would toss
your sorrow back in your face
shattered into a hundred,
a thousand different questions?

I don't know.
Is it reprieve
the journey's end should bring?
Or is it enough
simply to have gone away –
to have gone away so far
for so long that finally reprieve
is too gentle a word, too one-sided
for what you need,
for what you've already stepped toward.

Sujata Bhatt

Do Not Go Gentle Into That Good Night

Do not go gentle into that good night,
Old age should burn and rave at close of day;
Rage, rage against the dying of the light.

Though wise men at their end know dark is right,
Because their words had forked no lightning they
Do not go gentle into that good night.

Good men, the last wave by, crying how bright
Their frail deeds might have danced in a green bay,
Rage, rage against the dying of the light.

Wild men who caught and sang the sun in flight,
And learn, too late, they grieved it on its way,
Do not go gentle into that good night.

Grave men, near death, who see with blinding sight
Blind eyes could blaze like meteors and be gay,
Rage, rage against the dying of the light.

And you, my father, there on the sad height,
Curse, bless, me now with your fierce tears, I pray.
Do not go gentle into that good night.
Rage, rage against the dying of the light.

Dylan Thomas

Grown and Flown

I loved my love – alas to see
That this should be, alas!
I thought that this could scarcely be,
Yet has it come to pass:
Sweet sweet love was,
Now bitter bitter grown to me.

I loved my love from green of Spring
Until sere Autumn's fall;
But now that leaves are withering
How should one love at all?
One heart's too small
For hunger, cold, love, everything.

I loved my love on sunny days
Until late Summer's wane;
But now that frost begins to glaze
How should one love again?
Nay, love and pain
Walk wide apart in diverse ways.

Christina Rossetti

Bitch

Now, when he and I meet, after all these years,
I say to the bitch inside me, don't start growling.
He isn't a trespasser anymore,
just an old acquaintance tipping his hat.
My voice says, 'Nice to see you,'
As the bitch starts to bark hysterically.
He isn't an enemy now,
Where are your manners, I say, as I say,
'How are the children? They must be growing up.'
At a kind word from him, a look like the old days,
The bitch changes her tone: she begins to whimper.
She wants to snuggle up to him, to cringe.
Down, girl! Keep your distance
Or I'll give you a taste of the choke-chain.
'Fine, I'm just fine,' I tell him.
She slobbers and grovels.
After all, I am her mistress. She is basically loyal.
It's just that she remembers how she came running
Each evening, when she heard his step;
How she lay at his feet and looked up adoringly
Though he was absorbed in his paper;
Or, bored with her devotion, ordered her to the kitchen
Until he was ready to play.
But the small careless kindnesses
When he'd had a good day, or a couple of drinks,
Come back to her now, seem more important
Than the casual cruelties, the ultimate dismissal.
'It's nice to see you are doing so well,' I say.
He couldn't have taken you with him;
You were too demonstrative, too clumsy,
Not like the well-groomed pets of his new friends.

'Give my regards to your wife,' I say. You gag
As I drag you off by the scruff,
Saying, 'Goodbye! Goodbye! Nice to have seen you again.'

Carolyn Kizer

Part II,
Signs from the Old Times

from *Mental Fight*

II

What will we choose?
Will we allow ourselves to descend
Into universal chaos and darkness?
A world without hope, without wholeness
Without moorings, without light
Without possibility for mental fight,
A world breeding mass murderers
Energy vampires, serial killers
With minds spinning in anomie and amorality
With murder, rape, genocide as normality?
Or will we allow ourselves merely to drift
Into an era of more of the same
An era drained of significance, without shame,
Without wonder or excitement,
Just the same low-grade entertainment,
An era boring and predictable
'Flat, stale, weary and unprofitable'
In which we drift
In which we drift along
Too bored and too passive to care
About what strange realities rear
Their heads in our days and nights,
Till we awake too late to the death of our rights
Too late to do anything
Too late for thinking

About what we have allowed
To take over our lives
While we cruised along in casual flight
Mildly indifferent to storm or sunlight?

Ben Okri

Human Family

I note the obvious differences
in the human family.
Some of us are serious,
some thrive on comedy.

Some declare their lives are lived
as true profundity,
and others claim they really live
the real reality.

The variety of our skin tones
can confuse, bemuse, delight,
brown and pink and beige and purple,
tan and blue and white.

I've sailed upon the seven seas
and stopped in every land,
I've seen the wonders of the world,
not yet one common man.

I know ten thousand women
called Jane and Mary Jane,
but I've not seen any two
who really were the same.

Mirror twins are different
although their features jibe,
and lovers think quite different thoughts
while lying side by side.

We love and lose in China,
we weep on England's moors,
and laugh and moan in Guinea,
and thrive on Spanish shores.

We seek success in Finland,
are born and die in Maine.
In minor ways we differ,
in major we're the same.

I note the obvious differences
between each sort and type,
but we are more alike, my friends,
than we are unalike.

We are more alike, my friends,
than we are unalike.

We are more alike, my friends,
than we are unalike.

Maya Angelou

Notes

Crimewatch by Gavin Ewart

As our sessions in the Library progressed, we began to look more closely at different kinds of conflict. 'Crimewatch' appealed to me partly because of this. I like the fact that it deals with the subject on two initial levels. Firstly, on conflict within society (the many murders it speaks of) and secondly conflict within the supposedly 'meek and mild' human mind: the idea that these 'normal' people are fascinated by the 'lunatics' they see on programmes such as Crimewatch.

James Stevens

Empires by Douglas Dunn

This poem shows the conflicts between different empires and their leaders. The conflict between the leaders' orders and individual decisions is displayed. Death is also a strong theme in this poem. In battles between empires people always lose their lives, and all great civilisations eventually fall, to make way for new ones.

Francis Baker

The Dead by Sylvia Plath

I chose this poem as a tribute to the great artist that was Sylvia Plath. It is a poem that is engaging to me, as well as being a classic example of her style and voice. I believe that this poem speaks volumes about how some people view God and death, and how both are intertwined.

Charlie-Mai Norris

Ashes by Umberto Saba

I chose this Italian poem as I feel Saba effectively communicates his ideas on death through his depiction of heaven. I particularly enjoyed his mind-provoking images of life after death, which enabled me to emotionally engage myself with the poem.

Silvana D'Imperio

Your Sorrow by Sujata Bhatt

For me, this poem speaks of the reality of living with sorrow and the fact that although we move on, it always remains with us. The poet asks provoking questions and in admitting herself that she does not have the answers, encourages the reader to examine what effect they themselves expect time and experience to have on how they deal with their sorrow.

Anjuli Rogers

Do Not Go Gentle Into That Good Night by Dylan Thomas

I find this poem incredibly powerful as Thomas induces a certain confidence in himself into the reader. His use of the villanelle form provides an assertiveness that I think inspires the reader to 'fight', and his regular use of puns and the play on certain words create new dimensions for the poem.

Rebecca Stokes

Bitch by Carolyn Kizer

I chose this poem because it talks of the conflict someone has with their 'bitch', their inner self and inner voice. It is quite a humorous poem, personifying raw emotion as a dog, or in human terms, a 'bitch'. It talks about emotional conflict between the person and fighting back the feelings from a previous lover from a fresh reunion.

Metta Phommavongsa

Part II, Signs from the Old Times (from *Mental Fight*) by Ben Okri

This poem does not just tell us about the wrongs and illnesses of the world but it asks questions of us. It is ok to talk and write about war, pain, hate, conflict but what are we doing about it? If we just merely observe and carry on with our mundane lives while atrocities such as rape, slavery, genocides etc are going on, are we then any different to the people doing this?

Vivian Gagariga

112

Human Family by Maya Angelou

I like the message conveyed by this poem; that essentially we are all the same; that our skin colour is probably not the most different thing about us. Though our personalities may differ, we are all human, and should be treated equally.

Pearl Mackie

Index of Titles

Acknowledgements

The editors and publishers gratefully acknowledge permissions to use copyright material in this book as follows:

MAYA ANGELOU: to Virago Books for 'Caged Bird' and 'Human Family' from *The Complete Collected Poems* (Virago, 1994). MEG BATEMAN: to Birlinn Limited for 'Because I was so fond of him' from *Aotromachd agus dain eile - Lightness and other poems* (Polygon, 1997). SUJATA BHATT: to Carcanet Press for 'Your Sorrow' from *The Stinking Rose* (Carcanet,1995). ANDREW BUTTON: to the author for 'War Torn' from *Tide of Emotions* (Spotlight Poets, 1998). LEONARD COHEN: to Random House for 'As the Mist Leaves No Scar' from *Stranger Music* (Vintage Books, 1994). WENDY COPE: to Faber and Faber for 'Budgie Finds His Voice' from *Making Cocoa for Kingsley Amis* (Faber, 1986). IDRIS DAVIES: to Gomer Press for 'Waun Fair' from *Collected Poems* (Gomer, 2003). W.H. DAVIES: To Oxford University Press for 'Leisure' from *Selected Poems* (Oxford, 1985). MAURA DOOLEY: to Bloodaxe Books for 'Drought' from *Sound Barrier: Poems 1982-2002* (Bloodaxe, 2002): CAROL ANN DUFFY: to Anvil Press for 'Valentine' from *Mean Time* (Anvil, 1993). DOUGLAS DUNN: to Faber and Faber for 'Empires' from *New Selected Poems 1964-2000* (Faber, 2003). MENNA ELFYN: to Gomer Press for 'Esgidiau/Shoes' translated by Nigel Jenkins from *Eucalyptus: Selected Poems 1978-1994* (Gomer, 1995). GAVIN EWART: to Margo Ewart for 'Crimewatch' from *The Penguin Book of Poetry from Britain and Ireland since 1945* (Viking, 1998). RAYMOND GARLICK: to the author for 'Alys at the Zoo' from *Travel Notes* (Gomer, 1992). W.S.GRAHAM: to Margaret Snow for 'A Note to the Difficult One' from *New Collected Poems* (Faber, 2004). ROBERT GRAVES: to Carcanet Press for 'The Philosopher' from *Complete Poems Volume 2* (Carcanet, 1997). THOM GUNN: to Faber and Faber for 'Memory Unsettled' from *The Man With Night Sweats* (Faber, 1992). MIROSLAV HOLUB: to Vydal Odeon for 'Dveře' from *Sagitální Řez* (Odeon, 1988). To Bloodaxe Books for 'The door' translated by Ian Milner from *Poems Before and After* (Bloodaxe, 1987). DAVID HUGHES: to the author for 'Swonzee Boy See?' from *Tidy Boy* (Swansea Poetry Workshop, 1998). ROBERT HULL: to Peterloo Poets for 'For the Child Who Became Christopher' from *Encouraging Shakespeare* (Peterloo, 1993). KATHLEEN JAMIE: to the author and MacMillan for 'Lucky Bag' from *Jizzen* (Picador, 1999).